CHOOSING YOUR WAY THROUGH AMERICA'S PAST

BOOK 3

ADVENTURES

from 1850 - 1900

Anne E. Schraff

illustrated by Steven Meyers

J. WESTON WALCH PUBLISHER

PORTLAND, MAINE

Cover art: © *North Wind Picture Archives*
Untitled—Post-Civil War resettlement

Background: © *Erwin Raisz, Landforms of the United States*

1   2   3   4   5   6   7   8   9   10

ISBN 0-8251-2616-9

Copyright © 1990, 1991
J. Weston Walch, Publisher
P. O. Box 658 • Portland, Maine 04104-0658

Printed in the United States of America

Contents

Introduction

Most history books focus on famous people and reveal little about what the average person was doing at the time. This book highlights the courage, determination, and plain hard work of ordinary people, and it does so in an unusual way with adventures you participate in. Each adventure casts you as the central character and, at critical junctures, requires you to choose between options. Based on two sets of choices, each adventure has four possible outcomes—some tragic, some triumphant, just as they were for the real people of the times.

Your role is fictional, but the historical details are accurate. Each story is supplemented by a short passage containing interesting facts related to the period, a true/false or matching quiz, and two sets of suggested activities.

Other recommended activities include:

- Reviewing vocabulary before you read each story.

- Keeping a written record of your choices and the consequences of those choices.

- Discussing alternatives with others who chose different courses of action.

- Considering whether the protagonist is male or female. (In the majority of cases, the protagonist is sex-neutral.)

- Analyzing any effects this book has had on the way you make decisions and take risks.

- Writing a report on why it would, or would not, have been fun to live during this period of American history.

This book is intended for enjoyment as well as instruction. We hope that you will find it fun.

NORTH OR SOUTH?

It's the late 1850s, and you live on a Virginia plantation with your parents. Your older brother has moved to Boston, where he teaches Latin. Your home is a long wooden building with a columned portico (porch). The portico shades both the upstairs and the downstairs. How pleasant it is to sit out and sip lemonade on a warm afternoon!

You have spent this morning riding your favorite horse. Now you give him to the black stable boy and walk through your formal gardens. You stop to admire the pond in front of your house.

Your brother is home for a holiday, and he joins you on the porch. A black slave brings fresh anise cookies and lemon in spring water.

"Thank you, Will," you say with a smile. Will's mother almost raised you. She was like your second mother. You and Will played together as small children. You and your brother George and Will loved to pick blueberries and blackberries. You were just children playing then. Now you are Will's owner and he is your slave.

When Will goes away with the empty tray, Geoge says, "I am shocked by that! It just makes me ill!"

"What?" you ask in surprise.

"Slavery. Will is just as intelligent as we are! He reads Latin. Did you know that? Why should I be a teacher in college and he a slave?" George says.

You are surprised by your brother's anger. You never knew he felt like that! Why, he grew up here as you did. It must be ideas he learned in Boston! Still, you see the fairness in what he says. Will is smarter than you are! You will probably travel to Europe several times and have an

exciting life. You will choose what you will do. But Will must always be a slave. "George," you say now, "Father says the black people are better off as slaves. He says they are more like children."

"Nonsense!" George cries. "You should meet some free Negroes in Boston. I heard Frederick Douglass speak. He's the match of any white man in oratory!"

You *do* feel uncomfortable about it. But you always thought it was just the way things were. It was the natural way of life.

Suddenly George leans forward. "Come to New England with me! Just listen to Douglass speak. It will change your mind about many things!"

■ *If you go to New England, turn to page 3.*

■ *If you don't, turn to page 4.*

Find out what your fate is!

You are not looking forward to the trip to New England. You don't even tell your parents why you are going. Your father would have a heart attack! He thinks slavery is a benefit to both races. (It's true your family is very kind to its Negro slaves, but the blacks are still slaves.)

You tell your parents you just want to see New England. And then you travel to the North with George. One night, soon after you arrive in Boston, you go to a crowded hall. To the speaker's place comes a black man in a white shirt and frock coat. He looks about forty. He has stiff black hair and fiery eyes. When he begins speaking, his voice is stern and loud. He tells of beatings he received from his cruel masters. He shouts against the brutality of slavery.

You shift in your chair. You pull at your collar. Your family does not lash slaves like that! You treat them as members of the family. This Douglass fellow isn't talking about you and your family.

But then Douglass cries out against slavery itself! "Our souls boil with bitter anguish," he says.

George nudges you.

Douglass goes on, "We pray to God for deliverance from our chains! Slavery dehumanizes! It kills the soul!"

You are very upset after the lecture. You are sorry you came here. Douglass is a rabble-rouser. What does he want? Riots? The destruction of the whole agricultural system of the South? You turn to your brother as you walk home. "That man was not talking about us, George. Our Negroes are very happy and contented. You know they are. They would not want to be free. Remember how they always sing at their work?"

George laughs sharply. "Happy? Contented? I would say no. They sing about their sorrow. They sing about Heaven when they will at last be free. Even our old Mammy, Will's mother. I would find her crying by her cabin. She'd sing a lot, but she would have tears in her eyes. Would you want to be a slave? Would I? Never! No human being wants such a condition."

Suddenly George stops walking. He faces you. "Stay here with me! We will join the abolition society together. There is much work to do. It is a noble cause."

■ *If you stay with your brother, turn to page 5.*

■ *If you return to the South, turn to page 6.*

"I cannot go to New England. I have things to do here. There is no way of life as sweet as what we have here, George. Why, have you read the poetry of Alexander Meek?" you say.

George frowns. "Yes, and it's nonsense. Sentimental nonsense."

You rush inside and snatch up your copy of *Songs and Poems of the South*, by A.B. Meek. You read about flowers spreading treasures of crimson and snow, of the best gifts of Eden, "of the dear spell of your native home."

"It is not so sweet for the slaves," George snaps. "Come with me to the Hanford plantation. I will show you the true face of slavery."

Why—you know Zeb and Nellie Hanford. You often ride with their son, Nate. "I've been over there a lot, George. We have dined with them. Only last Sunday we ate roasted goose and heard Miss Lucy play the piano. It was a charming afternoon. What dark secrets do those lovely people hold?" you ask.

"Zeb Hanford is a brutal master who tortures the slaves. The dark crimes are hidden back in the shacks where the poor Negroes huddle. Come with me and see how charming and lovely Zeb is in the fields," George says.

"What vile slander! Really, George, New England has been no good for you. It has made you a stranger. It has made you an enemy of your own people!" you cry.

"Do you dare have a look for yourself?" George demands. "Right now Zeb will be in the fields. He wants to make sure every slave is giving the last drop of energy to the tasks. I have spoken to Will's cousin. He told me the cruellest overseer is mild beside Mr. Hanford."

You cannot believe there is truth in any of this. Mr. Hanford has always seemed to you to be a fine man. Yet your brother is daring you to come and see. You will not let George have the last word! (It's like when you were children. George would dare you to climb as high in the cherry tree as he did. You always took him up on it!)

But it seems dreadful to spy on your friend, Mr. Hanford!

■ *If you go to the Hanford plantation, turn to page 7.*

■ *If you don't, turn to page 8.*

As much as you love your home in Virginia, you cannot get over the words of Douglass. And you begin to remember things from your own childhood.

You played with a Negro boy named Peter. You would swim and chase rabbits together. Then Peter and his mother were sold. You cried and asked your father, "Where is Peter? Make Peter come. I want to play pirates."

Your father took you gently on his knee and said, "Don't fret, little one. Peter is now with his mother in Georgia. They were bought by another family. But we have bought a new Negro woman with two sons. You shall have two Peters instead of just one."

"But, Papa," you had cried, "I want *my* Peter!"

"The new Negro boys are just as lively as Peter. They shall be boon companions. And their mother can cook and sew so much better than Mamie, Peter's mother," your father said.

You cried all day over it. How could they sell Peter? But then you accepted it. It was the way of things. Now, suddenly, you remember your bitter sadness.

Peter ran away from his new master when he was fourteen. They caught him and branded him with a hot iron on his cheek. Your parents said it was sad, but Peter was "wild and unruly" and brought it on himself. You remember seeing how horrible the scar looked when you saw Peter. He turned his scarred face away from you. You found no friendship in his eyes.

"Yes," you say now. "You are right, George. I will send Father a letter. I'll tell him I want to go to school here too. But I will be working for the abolitionist cause. I must be a part of it. It's an important cause."

A big smile comes to George's face. "I knew I could count on you!" he says.

During the weeks and months ahead, you help edit a newspaper against slavery. You meet William Lloyd Garrison, who edits the abolitionist *Liberator*. You meet Henry David Thoreau and see an amazing incident.

There, in his Concord home, you see Thoreau and his sister Sophia hiding a runaway slave from Virginia! You are deeply touched. You are very glad you came North.

■ *Turn to page 9.*

"I won't listen to this! The abolitionists want to smash the South!" you cry. "Why, the poor factory workers here in the North live worse than our slaves."

George grabs your shoulder. "But they are free! I don't care how awful your life is. Where there is freedom there is hope!"

"Living in crowded huts? Sick with typhus? If they lose their jobs, they starve!" you shout. "Our slaves are cared for when they're old and sick. Remember how tenderly we cared for our old Maudie?"

"But they are not free!" George insists.

"Our Negroes are lucky! Lucky!" you almost scream.

You hurry to catch a carriage. You will go home by coach and railroad. You will never listen to such upsetting talk again!

On the last leg of your journey, you meet an older man. He sits opposite you on the train. You tell him of the Douglass speech you heard.

"Ah, he's a troublemaker. Wants to stir up riots and rebellion. They mean to cause bloodshed. It's a plot by the North. They have always wanted to get the best of the South! Now they want to stir up the Negroes," he says.

"I agree," you say.

In the fields beside the railroad tracks, black slaves pick cotton. They sing softly as they sway back and forth with their work. The older man smiles and says, "See there? Just what I mean. Did you ever see such contented folk? Like little children at play. What would they do without us? And what would we do without them?"

"You're right," you agree. But just then a white overseer appears. He has seen one of the slaves sitting down instead of working for a moment. It's very hot. Maybe the poor fellow felt sick or something.

The overseer strikes the man a terrible blow. You see him fall back. Then the train takes you away from the cotton fields.

You say nothing. The older man says nothing. You try to think of something else. Tonight you will be home. Your mother always serves pecan pie to celebrate a homecoming.

■ *Turn to page 9.*

You go with George to the Hanford plantation. It's not a long walk. You make the trip quickly.

"What do you think this will prove?" you demand.

"You'll see," George says.

Finally you arrive at the vast fields next to and behind the Hanford home. Black slaves are hoeing the soil for planting. Hanford raises vegetables for the family and tobacco as a main crop.

You see black and white overseers. They stand around with large hickory sticks and cowhide whips. You doubt that they use them that much. Mr. Hanford would not allow cruelty. But, of course, he's a good planter. He wants everyone to do their job right.

Then, as you watch, you see Zeb Hanford come out of the shade of a large oak. He carries a whip too. He shouts at one of the slaves—a woman. "Tell me, Hetty, does your son wear a new shirt? Was he allowed one?"

"No, Massa," the woman says, hanging her head. "The boy was naked and —"

"So you took what you had no right to, didn't you, Hetty? You know well that children who do not work are not allowed clothing. You stole from me, Hetty," he says sharply, striking the woman a hard blow with his whip.

"I'm sorry, Massa!" the woman cries.

"Would you like to be sold to Louisiana? You and your children put to picking cotton?" Mr. Hanford threatens.

"Oh, no, Massa," the woman cries, pleading and weeping.

"See that you don't wrong me again, Hetty," Mr. Hanford says sharply.

You shrink in horror. You never dreamed Mr. Hanford was capable of such cruelty!

Suddenly Mr. Hanford spots you and your brother. He comes over smiling. "Well, good afternoon." He wipes beads of sweat off his brow. He sees you staring at the weeping slave woman and he says, "She's a terrible thief. If she were not punished frequently she would rob me constantly."

You feel sick. But should you give up your good life in Virginia and go off to New England over such a thing? What is this to you? You don't even know this slave woman who has been struck . . . .

You are turning to go home when you see one of the overseers tearing the shirt from the back of Hetty's three-year-old son.

Your voice trembles when you speak. "I will come North with you, George," you say.

■ *Turn to page 9.*

"Oh, off with you, George. I will not spy like an enemy on our neighbors! The North has made a fanatic of you."

Shaking his head, George leaves for New England.

At dinner, you raise the question of slavery with your father. "Ah," your father responds. "George has been turned against our whole way of life in Boston. He is now critical of our traditions. Dreadful, lying books like *Uncle Tom's Cabin* have inflamed people's minds. Dirty little book! It's an outrage!" your father raves.

You nod.

"You know the Negro is nothing but a grown-up child. Why, we do them a favor by caring for them and telling them what to do," your father goes on.

"Father . . . Will seems very intelligent," you say.

"Indeed, as are children. But emotionally he is a child. He is happy here. He depends on us like a young child," your father says.

"I guess so," you say. Poor Will would probably hate it if slavery ended. What would he do? You smile at the idea of the slaves on their own. How could they take care of themselves, poor things!

"Speaking of Will," your father says, "where is he? I rang the bell for dessert. He ought to be here with the strawberry cake and cream." Your father rings the bell again.

But Will does not come. Two other servants are sent to find him.

"Massa," says Louis, one of the servants, "Will is gone. He has run away, I'm afraid."

"Impossible!" your father thunders. He slams his fist on the table. "He would not run away. He was too happy here. He was like one of the family. There must be some mistake!"

In three months you receive a letter from Canada. It is written in Will's hand.

"Sir," he writes your father, "I know you regard me with ill will, but I had to leave. Here in Canada I am free to use the talents God has graciously given me. I wish your family well. I pray you will one day regard me as highly as I regard you. Your humble servant, Will Walters."

You don't think it was coincidence that Will left the same time your brother did. You can't help it, but you are proud of George. But you are even more proud of Will.

He chose freedom.

■   *Turn to page 9.*

The Exodusters

Benjamin "Pap" Singleton was born in Tennessee in 1809. He was a slave who ran away from his master. He went to Canada until the Civil War freed the slaves. Singleton came home then. He decided the freed slaves would be happier in Kansas. So in 1873 Pap Singleton led three hundred black people to a new colony in Kansas.

That was only the beginning. Pretty soon thousands came from South Carolina, Mississippi, and Louisiana. They came by boat, rail, and horseback. Almost twenty thousand moved to Kansas. It was called the exodus of 1879. *Exodus* is a word from the Bible that describes the Jews' journey to the promised land.

Pap's exodusters did not find the promised land in Kansas. But they liked it well enough to stay.

Matching

1. A portico is a(n)

   _____ .

2. Pap Singleton was a(n)

   _____ .

3. The black orator in Boston was

   _____ .

4. The slave Will was able to read in

   _____ .

5. There were free Negroes in the city of

   _____ .

a) Frederick Douglass

b) porch

c) Boston

d) exoduster

e) Latin

Group Activities

1. Find a map showing the states that seceded from the Union. Note the date each state left.

2. Discuss the reasons for and against a young Virginian becoming an abolitionist or staying loyal to the South.

3. Play recordings in class of the speeches of Frederick Douglass. Then discuss his ideas.

Individual Activities

1. Imagine you are an escaping slave on the Underground Railroad. Explain why you were not happy even under a kind master.

2. Read a portion of *Uncle Tom's Cabin*. Write a paragraph about it.

3. Read about a famous abolitionist in a history book. Then write a paragraph about her or him.

AFTER THE BUFFALO

It's 1864 and you are a young Cheyenne. The buffalo herds have been the life of your people. From their flesh you have had meat. Buffalo tongue and liver are especially delicious. Buffalo hide has given you clothing, tepees, robes, moccasins, saddles, even dolls. Buffalo bones give you tools. Buffalo hair makes your rope.

Your men and boys have taken only the buffalo that you need to live. But now the whites have come. White hunters and white settlers have destroyed the great herds of buffalo. Once the buffalo are totally gone, what will become of the Cheyenne, your people? What will become of you, a young person?

"Already there are Cheyenne and Arapaho chiefs who have gone to the reservation," your father says. Your father is chief of your tribe. "They have led their people to the reservation. They are now as dead. They are penned up like dogs."

First the gold-seekers came in 1849. You were a very small child then. The whites seemed wild with gold fever. Now the settlers come. They say buffalo leather is good for making shoes and belts. They kill as many buffalo as they can.

Your father's face is sad as he speaks. "Will we lose our freedom too? Will we be penned up like dogs?"

You know what a brave warrior your father is. He has fought with his ball-and-spike-head club. But the whites are like ants on sugar. There are so many of them and so few of you!

"Black Kettle and White Antelope speak of peace. They got to a camp at Sand Creek. They tell us to come too. They say the whites will let us be there. Is it an old man's fear that makes peace

look so good? Tell me, young one, what are your ideas?"

You cannot imagine a life different from the one you have always known. You love your wild, free life. You love the races and dice games. But the white man's muskets spit out a quick death. Maybe if you went to Sand Creek you might stay free and at peace. Or is it a trap?

■ *If you suggest going to Sand Creek, turn to page 13.*

■ *If not, turn to page 14.*

Find out what your fate is!

"Black Kettle and White Antelope are wise chiefs, aren't they, Father?" you ask.

He nods. "They say the whites will leave us alone at Sand Creek. We will not be forced into the reservation if we stay there. They tell me the Indians may camp peacefully at Fort Lyon or nearby on Sand Creek."

"Then let us go there," you say.

"It is also my thought," your father says. "The whites have promised rations for the winter. We shall have no dying as the snow falls."

You travel to Sand Creek. You see two flags flying. One is a white flag for peace. The other is an American flag. "Those flags," explains Black Kettle, "will protect us from soldiers."

There are about five hundred Cheyenne men, women, and children here. They gather buffalo robes for the winter cold. You walk among them, worry stirring your heart.

Can the whites be trusted? What if the soldiers told you to come here only to attack you?

A young Cheyenne says to you, "The Colorado soldier—the big general—has said they will fight us until we are finished. I think this is so. We are not safe. Sometime when we expect no trouble, it will come down on us like a storm."

"But the white commander said no soldiers will attack us here," you point out.

Your companion laughs. "I see this place as a trap. My family will pack and go from here. We have no taste for winter fighting, but death is in the wind. I would rather meet the white man warrior to warrior than be caught asleep! Even the medicine man who speaks to the spirit world warns of trouble here."

The words of the young man disturb you. What if it's true?

You go looking for your father. You find him huddled in his buffalo robe. He looks weary and half asleep. Should you disturb him with your own worries?

■ *If you urge your father to leave, turn to page 15.*

■ *If not, turn to page 16.*

"Father, I have a bad feeling about this Sand Creek," you say.

Your father nods his gray head. "In my heart I wish to go there. In my head, I fear you are right. A wise man listens more to his head than his heart. I respect your words, young one."

You remain in your small camp in the hills. As night falls, you gather around small fires and listen to the old ones talk. Tonight the talk is of the grizzly bear.

"His razor-sharp claws might tear a man apart. But the bear is to be honored. He has great power. Even when we kill the grizzly bear we must tell him we are sorry. We must say lack of food has driven us to this deed. No bear must ever be killed when there is no need," says an ancient hunter of your tribe.

In the weeks that follow, you hear the sad fate of the Indians who went to Sand Creek. White soldiers rode in and killed most of the Cheyenne camping there. Even a flag of peace did no good!

Then the terrible moment arrives for you and your family. Many soldiers come, and you are driven to Oklahoma. You find a barren land between the Arkansas and Cimarron rivers. Strange fevers occur there. It is a sandy wasteland in the summer heat. Even the streams dry up. In winter icy winds howl. But at least there is peace.

You hear of other battles between Cheyenne warriors and white soldiers. But the cause of the Cheyenne is lost. The buffalo herds are gone.

The Indian agents give you hoes and plows. "Walk the white man's way," you are told. But you are hunters, not farmers!

In the late 1870s, you are offered the chance to go to Pennsylvania and learn agricultural and mechanical subjects. Only a few young Cheyenne, Pawnee and Kiowa will have this chance. You are very lucky, they tell you. But is it the right thing to go?

■ *If you go, turn to page 17.*

■ *If not, turn to page 18.*

You share your fears with your father. He listens and nods. "I too have heard frightening predictions from the medicine man," your father says. "We will go."

Your father leads you and his band of Cheyenne from Sand Creek into the mountains. You will not be completely safe anywhere. But at least now the whites will not know where you are.

A few days later, Black Kettle and a few young warriors ride into your camp. Their eyes are wild with hate.

"All dead!" cries Black Kettle. "Our women—our children—most of our warriors are dead!"

"What happened?" you ask.

"The white Colonel Chivington rode into camp as we slept. They charged, firing and bayonetting. I raised the American flag. Then I raised the white flag. They went on killing," wails Black Kettle.

You feel rage boiling in your blood. Your father curses the treachery of the whites.

All through the winter of 1864, the Cheyenne warriors take revenge on white settlements because of Sand Creek. Your people rip out telegraph wires and ride against ranches. You hear the screams of white settlers and see bloody scalps.

One dark night, the soldiers come to your camp. After all the raids by Cheyenne warriors, you are not surprised. You fight against the soldiers, but they are many. You see your father fall dead, and then your mother. Before you die yourself, you remember many things. You think of your fine tipi covered with sewn buffalo hide. You remember the porcupine embroidery and beadwork that brightened your clothing. Most of all, you remember the happy times. There was much buffalo meat for feasting and there was dancing and storytelling.

You know you would not have liked life on the reservation. So when the bullet enters your heart, you die without a struggle. It was perhaps more merciful than life would have been for you.

■ *Turn to page 19.*

You decide not to worry your father with your fears. Sand Creek will probably be a safe winter home. When spring comes, who knows what will happen?

On November 29, 1864, troops commanded by Colonel J. M. Chivington surround the camp. You are sleeping and do not see them come. As dawn arrives, Chivington and his soldiers attack! You see Black Kettle raise the American flag.

Chivington's men are firing away. The flag does not stop them. Then Black Kettle raises the white flag. Still the killing goes on!

You rush with your companions across the camp to the high banks of the hillside. You see women and small children screaming and running everywhere. A few are hiding in a small cave. The soldiers go in and kill them! Little children are beaten to death with rifle butts!

Some warriors escape. They cannot stop the massacre, but they can take revenge later on. Your parents are dead when you flee with Black Kettle. Four hundred and fifty others are dead too!

Your heart burns with a terrible hatred. You hear that Colonel Chivington has returned to Denver as a hero. He has Indian horses and scalps and everybody cheers him.

The next year your chiefs sign a peace treaty with the whites. You must go south of the Arkansas River onto lands of the Kiowa. You want no part of this! You join the rebel Cheyenne who travel with Black Kettle. You and your companions arrive at the Washita River.

On November 27, 1868, General George Armstrong Custer attacks Black Kettle's camp. The Cheyenne warriors fight gallantly. Still, fifty-one lodges are destroyed. Over one hundred Cheyenne are killed. But again you survive. You now leave Black Kettle and his wife among the dead.

You are alive in June of 1876 when the most famous of all battles is fought between the Indians and the whites. At the Little Big Horn in Montana, the Cheyenne and Sioux kill General Custer and two hundred and sixty of his soldiers. At last a victory!

But the good times of the buffalo and the hunting life never return. Eventually you too must go to a hated reservation. You grieve over your lost way of life. And you tell the children about the battle of the Little Big Horn over and over again.

■   *Turn to page 19.*

You feel you are giving in to the whites' way. But what else can you do? The Cheyenne way as it used to be is gone. The last hope was lost when the Union Pacific laid railroad track over Indian hunting lands. Cheyenne warriors tried to rip up the tracks at night. They attacked engineers. But it was a losing battle. Now white settlers shoot the last of the buffalo from the railroad cars!

You learn how to be a teacher. Then you return to the reservation to teach others. You teach the young Cheyenne respect and love for the Cheyenne traditions. But you also tell them, "The world is different now. We must make our lives in this new world. The wild, free life is gone."

One boy comes to you and says, "I will get a rifle and a horse and fight the whites. We will ride again. The mountains will fill with our war screams. We will find our old hunting lands in Montana."

"No," you tell the boy sadly. "There are no more hunting lands. No more buffalo."

You see that some of your students hate you. They think you have turned away from the Cheyenne way. They think you have become a white person in your heart. But you have only tried to help the children live in this new world.

"Be proud that you are Indian," you say. "You have much to teach other people. We have respect for nature. We must teach it to others. We try to care for the earth and all its creatures. This is something all must learn. We see death as the start of a better life. We have a strong religion. To us, the land belongs to all. Nobody must be hungry if somebody has food. Be proud of these good things in your heart."

Most of your students listen to your words. You see their eyes shine. You have taught them to like themselves. This is maybe the most important thing you teach them. It will carry them through the hard times ahead. You are happy to have become a teacher.

■ *Turn to page 19.*

You have no wish to go to a white school. You don't want to learn ways that you hate.

Your life settles down to a dull routine. Mostly you sit in your tipi on the reservation and talk about the old days. You never get tired of talking about the wild, free life in Montana.

Your father is now very old. He and the other old chiefs sit around the fires and brag of their victories in battle. Some tell of battles that never were fought.

"I was at the Little Big Horn," says your father, "and I saw the yellow-haired General Custer die!"

Your face turns red in shame. Your father was not at the Little Big Horn when Custer was killed!

Another old chief laughs mockingly. "You were not at that battle, old one. You sat wrapped in your buffalo robe while others won the great victory," he says.

Your father grows angry. It breaks your heart to see him like this. The others make fun of him. He curses them and walks off alone, across the bleak land.

When your father does not come back before dark, you look for him. You spend hours walking the hard, cold land.

At last, near midnight, you find your father. He is lying in a frozen creek bed. His face is pale with death. His face is calm. His lips are parted a little. Even now you see the brave warrior who rode the plains shouting fiercely. In the still, cold air you can hear your father's shouts as he would leave for the hunt. Your father was a handsome man with long raven hair. A few gray hairs on his head now glint in the moonlight.

You carry your father to his burial with an aching heart. After that, you do not do much. You will not farm this land. You stare into the blue sky and live off the rations the government gives you. You have no more tears to shed. You have little wish to live.

The only good times you have are when you dream of Montana. But the memories grow dimmer.

One day, around the fire, you say you fought at the battle of the Little Big Horn.

The others laugh at you. You were too young for that, they say. You are a liar.

You walk across the bleak land, alone.

■ *Turn to page 19.*

Sign Language

The Plains Indians were made up of many tribes. As they hunted over wide areas, they met hunters from other tribes. They all spoke different languages. So they needed a common language to understand one another. This was sign language.

A Crow Indian would identify himself as Crow in this way: He would rub his left hand back and forth from wrist to knuckles with his right hand. Then he would hold his fist above his forehead.

A Cheyenne Indian would rub his left hand in the same way. But then he would chop his left index finger with his right hand.

The language of the Indians also included signals such as smoke, waving blankets, and use of mirrors. The U.S. Signal Corps later based their signaling system on the language of the Comanche Indians.

True/False

_____ 1. The Plains Indians used the buffalo only for food.

_____ 2. The U.S. Signal Corps based its signals on the language of the Cheyenne.

_____ 3. In 1849 whites came to the Cheyenne lands looking for oil.

_____ 4. Black Kettle went to the camp at Sand Creek.

_____ 5. White Antelope was the chief who refused to go to the camp at Sand Creek.

Group Activities

1. Learn some Indian sign language by consulting library books. You and your classmates might tell stories using sign language. Here is a simple one:
   1. Raise four fingers. (Four years ago . . .
   2. Raise right fist over head. (the white man . . .
   3. Hold out open right hand. (friends . . .
   4. Hold open right hand over heart. (with us . . .
   5. Lower right hand below heart. (a lie!
   6. Make fists with both hands, hold out. (Done, finished, that is all.)

2. Find Indian legends in library books. Tell one to the rest of the class, which is gathered around in a circle, sitting cross-legged on the floor.

3. Play the Johnny Cash album *Bitter Tears* in class, discussing each song.

Individual Activities

1. Indians told stories or gave messages using simple pictures carved on trees. Using your imagination, make simple statements using pictures.

2. Imagine you are a young Cheyenne in the 1860s. Explain why you would or would not adopt the whites' ways.

3. Write a paragraph about one of these great Plains Indian leaders:
   Roman Nose   Washakie   Black Kettle
   Crazy Horse   Sitting Bull   Gall

AFTER THE WAR

It's the autumn of 1867 and you are a young Southerner. You must labor in the fields of your once-fine South Carolina plantation. When you were small, black slaves did this work. You sat on the broad, columned porch and watched. Your older brothers and sisters went off to fine parties or horseback riding. Your family owned a nice carriage. You loved traveling in the countryside to see the spring blossoms or the autumn colors.

When you were a toddler, your kindly black nurse made you cornhusk dolls. She even made you a juggling board on the veranda (porch). It was a loose board suspended between brackets. What a pleasant, easygoing life it was! You dined on turtle soup, ham, roast turkey, hot biscuits, apple pie, cheese, and fruit.

Now it's all gone. Your beautiful home was stripped of all its furniture during the Civil War. The smokehouse and laundry were burned down. The rows of slave cabins still stand, though they are empty. The doors bang open and shut in the wind. All your slaves were freed. They all rushed off but one. Louis, your half-blind house servant, is still with you. Your father and brother died in the war. Now you struggle to stay alive. You grow a few vegetables and keep chickens. You shoot game when you can.

"What will become of us?" your poor, sad mother wails. She is very bitter that the black slaves all left. Now she thinks they are taking over the South. You have seen many former slaves roaming the countryside. Many are starving. They have no skills. Nobody will hire them. Something called the Freedmen's Bureau tries to help a little. But you have seen wagons full of wooden painted coffins carry dead black people to the black cemetery. They died of hunger or consumption from being out in the cold.

Still, there is a black man right here in town who is trying to get elected to the House of Representatives. "Imagine!" your mother says. "A Negro slave from South Carolina wanting to rule over us! Can you imagine such a nerve?" (The truth is, Mr. Bolter is a free Negro from New York.)

A local group of white people want put a stop to this. You wonder how it would be to have black politicians. You aren't sure how you feel deep down.

■ *If you join the local group, turn to page 23.*

■ *If not, turn to page 24.*

Find out what your fate is!

You meet one night with a group of young and old neighbors. The meeting is held behind some scrub pines. Some war veterans are there. Some former plantation owners are there too. But most of the people are small farmers. They were poor even before the war. Now they are even worse off. They want to blame somebody. They hate the Northerners. They hate the black people too.

"They're working together," one man says. "The North won the war. Now they mean to crush us. They're gonna use black people to do it. They want to put the slaves over us."

A red-faced, angry-looking woman nods. "The North means to grind us down with Negro soldiers. And Negro politicians," she says.

"How many here haven't got enough to eat?" a man with a yellow beard asks.

You raise your hand. Everybody else does too.

"How many here are scared of losing their homes to the tax man?" the yellow-bearded man asks.

Again you all raise your hands.

"That Negro fellow who wants to be in the House of Representatives," says the leader, "he wants to tax all the white folks. We won't have nothing to eat. We won't be able to pay our taxes. You want that to happen?"

"No!" everybody shouts.

"We gonna do something about that uppity Negro?" the leader asks.

"Yes!" people shout.

"Our boys fought real bravely in the war. We owe it to them to stand up to what's happening," the plantation owner says.

"The Yankees mean to make an end to the Southern way of life!" the red-faced woman cries.

"I'd rather have died in the war than have Negro overlords!" cries an army veteran with just one leg.

You keep silent. But you remember the old days. You remember the wonderful life. Still, you don't hate the Negroes who ran off to freedom. You would have done the same thing in their place. But, at the same time, you are afraid. What if the Northern soldiers turn the former slaves against you white people?

"The Negroes will have all the guns!" shouts the yellow-bearded man. "And they'll be in the State House. We'll be nothing! I say we ride over to Ed Bolter's house and teach him a lesson. We don't aim to be ruled by Negroes like him!"

■ *If you go with the others, turn to page 25.*

■ *If not, turn to page 26.*

You can't see how joining this group would help your family. Maybe you ought to go north yourself and get a job. Then you could send money home.

"I could go to Baltimore and work," you say. "Surely there is work for an industrious young person like me in that big city."

"You go to the city alone? Oh! That distresses me!" your mother groans. "If only there was a way to earn money from this land again!"

"You and Louis might try to hire back some of our old slaves," you say. You see them wandering about aimlessly. You could not pay them wages. You have no money. But you could offer them room and board and part of the crops when they come in. Owners are putting in new crops like tobacco. Even wheat and fruit are being grown along with vegetables. The Yankees took a lot away, but you still have the land, don't you?

"You must stay and help us," your mother says.

"But what if the plantation fails? Even if everyone works hard, it still might fail. Then we will have no cash. If I go to Baltimore, there will surely be cash," you argue.

But deep in your heart you are afraid to go to Baltimore alone. You have lived around here all your life. It must be frightening to be alone in a big city like that. What if you become ill? Who will help you?

Yet Baltimore is a great lure. Many are going there from Virginia and South Carolina. You have heard that it's an exciting city. There are large, handsome homes and amusements you have never seen. You are eager to see more of the world than you have thus far seen. A bright future may wait for you in Baltimore. And wouldn't it be wonderful to send money home? Your mother would not have to worry anymore. There would be money and time enough to rebuild the plantation home.

■ *If you go to Baltimore, turn to page 27.*

■ *If not, turn to page 28.*

You ride off into the night with the others. You head for the Bolter family house. You don't know Mr. Bolter. He was never a slave. He was born in New York. After the Civil War, he came to live in South Carolina. Now he wants to be a politician.

Mr. Bolter claims he is educated. You don't know about that. He's been living in South Carolina about two and a half years. Why didn't he stay in New York with the other Yankees?

The small frame Bolter house stands behind two oak trees. A light flickers inside. The yellow-bearded man jumps off his mule and pounds on the door. "Open up in there!" he shouts.

You see somebody peeking from around the window. It looks like a black woman. "Go away!" she shouts. "I got a child here."

"Tell the black Yankee to come out!" somebody yells. You hear a child crying inside the house. You feel nervous. You are sorry you came here tonight.

Suddenly you smell fire! One of the men has lit a stick and he's moving around the side of the house. He's setting fire to the house!

The front door springs open and there is Mr. Bolter. He's a big, tall man. He's so dark you could never mistake him for white. "You get off my property," he says. "You're nothing but lawbreakers."

Now the mob is really mad. They don't want a Negro scolding them. Soon burning sticks are landing on the roof. The men surge forward and grab Mr. Bolter. The whole house is on fire, and the woman and child flee out the back way. Mr. Bolter is tied to one of the big oaks. His shirt is ripped off. He is whipped bloody. When they finally cut Mr. Bolter down, he stumbles off into the woods.

By now the burning roof timbers fall inside the house. The windows explode out. Everybody cheers.

"Isn't that a splended sight?" asks the former plantation owner. "I am jubilant! This is the first time I have known happiness since Appomattox [the surrender of the South to the North at the end of the Civil War]."

You just feel sick. You hurry home, sad and ashamed. The Bolters are never seen in town again. The terror worked. But another black man is elected later to the House of Representatives from this district. He is not educated like Mr. Bolter. He does not do nearly as good a job as Bolter would have done.

■ *Turn to page 29.*

You just don't like mobs. You hurry home and sit on a wicker chair on your porch. Your mother comes out to sit beside you. Then Louis comes with a tray of cool drinks. You don't know how Louis does it. He always seems to have lemons for cool drinks!

"I really feel bad, Missus," Louis says. "Them Yankees took all your fine things. Even set fire to the fences."

"Yes, Louis. They had no manners at all. But you have been so loyal. The others . . . Jim, Jeb, even Lucy . . . they told the Yankees where our silver was . . . and the jewelry. Oh, it broke my heart when they turned on us like that," your mother says, dabbing at her eyes.

"Yes, Missus. They were no good, that bunch," Louis says.

Just then, a black man and his wife and son come hurrying across the field. The moon is bright. You can see blood streaming from the man's shirt.

"Why, it's that Mister Bolter who wants to be in the Congress," your mother gasps.

"Looks like the mob got to him," you say with a shudder. He has been whipped!

"Lordy, he's bleeding, Missus," Louis says.

Your mother gets up and goes down the porch steps. She can't stand to see anybody hurting. She tells you and Louis, "Go and get clean rags and hot water."

When you come back with the water and rags, the Bolters are in your parlor. The little boy is trying not to cry. "They burned our house down," Mrs. Bolter tells you.

Your mother sponges off the bloody wounds on Mr. Bolter's back. She and Mrs. Bolter bind them with clean rags. Some of the whip cuts are very deep.

"I want to be a Congressman to help Negroes and white folks," says Mr. Bolter. "We are all in need of help. I want free schools for all the children. I want to fix the roads and the buildings and the railroad tracks so we can ship our products again. Why, most of the railroad tracks are wrapped around trees now! [The Union soldiers often heated the tracks and wrapped them around trees during the war.] I want the South to be a good place for all of us to live."

The Bolters thank you and hurry off then. You never see them again. Mr. Bolter does not get elected to the House of Representatives. But two years later another black man does. He is not as intelligent as Mr. Bolter was. So he does not do a very good job.

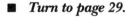 ■ *Turn to page 29.*

You bid a tearful farewell to your mother. Louis promises to take care of her. Your mother pleads with you not to go. But you can tell she is proud of you too. You are taking a bold step. She is proud of your independence and courage.

When you arrive in Baltimore, you visit with a friend who already works in a fine home. You cannot believe how well the rich of Baltimore live! They eat terrapins (turtles), soft crabs, and canvasback ducks for dinner. They dress very stylishly too. They go the theaters all the time, and talented people gather in clubs. The life of the rich reminds you of the life you once had back home.

With the help of your friend, you get a job in a public house (inn and restaurant). You are a food-server. Your work is much like the work of the Negro slaves who used to serve you and your family. But you can send money home right away. You are very proud of that.

After two years, you move from Baltimore to Chicago. You now work as a cook in a fine hotel. You make even better wages and send a lot of money home.

One warm, windy day in October of 1871, you see a big plume of smoke in the sky over Chicago. You live in a rented room in a pine house. You aren't worried that the fire will come here. It is too far away. And many horse-drawn wagons race with water to put it out. Still the wind grows stronger. Sparks and burning debris fly overhead.

By midnight, twenty city blocks are burning! The houses have pine fences. The streets are covered with pine blocks. The sidewalks have pine planks. The fire eats up pine like crazy. The flames move like great ocean waves. Sometimes they leap two hundred feet.

You rush with hundreds of your neighbors to the waterfront. You stand there and watch buildings melt. It's almost like the fires of the Civil War around your home!

Then, at last, on Monday night, the rain comes. By Tuesday morning the disaster is over. Three hundred people are dead. Thousands of buildings are gone. You have lost all your possessions. But you don't despair. You find immediate work helping to rebuild Chicago. You go on to better jobs and more money. You go home now only to visit because you love Chicago. You want to spend the rest of your life here.

■ *Turn to page 29.*

You decide to stay in South Carolina and help your mother and Louis rebuild the plantation. Along with Louis, you search out many of your old slaves. You find four of them huddled in the remains of an old smokehouse. They have been living on a few bags of corn they found. Now there's nothing left. They are stripping off tree bark to eat.

"You boys come along with us and work," Louis says. "There will be cash when the crop comes in. Meanwhile, you can live in the old cabins and we can give you rations."

The four of them come with you. You find three more and you go home with them. Now you have seven workers. You can rebuild the broken-down buildings and start a crop. You plant corn and vegetables and some fruit trees.

Your first crop isn't bountiful (rich), but it gives you enough cash to buy more supplies. Each of the black workers gets a small wage too. You are encouraged. Your life is far from what it used to be. But now there is at least hope.

As time goes by, you buy some chickens and turkeys. Your main cash crop turns out to be eggs. Your peach trees are producing fruit too. You sell cabbages and beans and sweet potatoes. You experiment with different crops.

When you have enough money to buy a new wagon, you ride along the old familiar roads. What memories they hold! The ugly signs of war are gone now. Sturdy little saplings are growing into new trees. The meadows are green and the springs are bubbling. The birds are singing again. There's that old sweet smell of jasmine in the soft night.

"It's going to be all right again, Louis," you say to the old black man beside you.

"It's going to be better," he says with a smile.

"Yes," you admit. And you know it will be. You are very glad you stayed in South Carolina. You will be one of the young people who build the new South. The great new South of tomorrow.

■ *Turn to page 29.*

One Plantation in Virginia

During the Civil War, many landholdings of the Confederate people were taken over by the federal government. After the war, the government paid for the land it took. General Robert E. Lee, the most famous Confederate general, owned a large plantation in Arlington, Virginia. The government paid $26,800 for this beautiful piece of land. The government turned it into Arlington National Cemetery.

Now buried here are thousands of soldiers from the North and South. Most of the men who fell in the Battle of Bull Run are here. They are all unknown soldiers. The bodies were buried all together with one single monument. Soldiers, sailors, marines, men and women from other wars are buried here too. Over 127,000 Americans lie at Arlington. Also buried here are two presidents, William Howard Taft and John F. Kennedy.

Matching

1. Arlington was once owned by

   _____ .

2. Agency set up to help ex-slaves in the South:

   _____ .

3. Presidents buried at Arlington are

   John F. Kennedy and _____ .

4. Almost everyone who fell in this battle is

   buried at Arlington: _____ .

5. Arlington is in this state:

   _____ .

a) Freedmen's Bureau

b) Virginia

c) Bull Run

d) William H. Taft

e) Robert E. Lee

Group Activities

1. Cotton planted year after year ruined the soil in many southern states. Read about the climate of South Carolina. Make a list of crops other than cotton that have been successful there. You can find this information in encyclopedias.

2. Discuss which of the following groups probably had the hardest time after the Civil War:

   Former plantation owners   Former slaves

3. Students who chose going to Baltimore should discuss the advantages and disadvantages of that choice with those who chose to stay in South Carolina.

Individual Activities

1. Many blacks were elected to political office in the South after the Civil War. Some did good jobs; others were not educated enough to govern. Write about one of the following black politicians:
    Hiram Revels   Blanche Bruce   Richard Cain
    Robert Elliott   John Lynch   Jefferson Long

2. The cost of living in the 1850s and 1860s is reflected in the prices of these products:
    Bushel of potatoes—50¢
    1 lb. sugar—8¢
    2 lbs. butter—31½¢
    Find out what these items cost today.

TENEMENT FOLK

You are a young German immigrant living in New York in 1889. Most of the others in the dirty, crowded tenement are Jewish like you. You came here with your brother and your father a few years ago. Your brother has moved away and your father has died. You have worked hard as a shirt-maker. You have saved a little money. Now you want to move to a different city.

You share a room in a four-story tenement with another family. This place is an oven in summer and an icebox in winter. Disease is widespread. Tuberculosis, diphtheria, and small-pox strike often. The place is called a "den of death."

You have a cousin who has moved to Pittsburgh. He writes glowing letters.

"Dear Cousin, I have a good factory job. There are many good jobs here. I found out there are thirty-five miles of factories. People here make objects of iron, steel, cotton, brass, everything! Jobs are plentiful for men and women."

You talk about Pittsburgh to a friend in the tenement. "Oh, no. Such a dirty city! Smoky! *Oy*, it is very, very sooty and grimy. My uncle is there. He is moving to Chicago. Now there is a fine city," your friend says.

"So what is good about Chicago?" you ask.

"Well, it is a big, growing place. My uncle says there are so many new buildings. The sound of hammers is like thunder. There is a big wholesale and shopping district. Trains flash by constantly!"

"Perhaps I will go there," you say.

"Yes, this Chicago is like a magnet. It draws all ambitious people," your friend says. "When I have enough saved I am going there too."

You are eighteen years old. You are sure you don't want to stay here in this New York tenement. But will you take a train to Pittsburgh or to Chicago?

///

- *If you go to Pittsburgh, turn to page 33.*

- *If you go to Chicago, turn to page 34.*

Find out what your fate is!

You arrive in Pittsburgh, and the first look at it surprises you. Pittsburgh lies in a hollow among hills and rivers. The city gleams with a strange light. But the most amazing things are the blast furnaces. Fire streams into the smoky sky day and night. It reminds you of fire-breathing dragons in the storybooks of your childhood.

"It's like hell!" gasps an old woman.

You shudder a little. "Yes," you agree.

You find a small room and begin to search for work. Pittsburgh is a drab, murky place even at midday. Most of your neighbors work at the foundry. It's hard, dirty work, but the pay is good. Your cousin works at a foundry. He has a room down the street from you.

"Aren't you afraid of working there?" you ask him. "Isn't it dangerous?"

"Oh, yes," he says. "Some workers are hurt. Some are killed. You must be very careful. But I make enough to save some money. I make twenty cents a day more than I made at the glassworks. I can put all that away for the future."

"But," you say, "you wanted to be a glassmaker like your father. Don't you remember when we were children how you told me that? 'I will be a glassmaker' was what you always said."

"Yes, yes," your cousin says a little impatiently. "Those were the dreams of a child. Now we are grown, eh? Right now I will work at the foundry and save money. Then later will be time for glassmaking."

You search for a job almost every waking hour. Finally you find a low-paying job in a cotton factory. It's dark and hard to breathe in the factory. But it's the best you can do.

"At least we will not be killed like the poor people in the foundries," a fellow worker says.

Your heart turns to ice. Your beloved cousin is in danger. You must try to convince him to leave his dangerous job.

You eat supper together that night. You once again try to convince your cousin to leave the foundry.

"No, no. Not yet. Come, let us talk of pleasant things," your cousin says.

■ *If you quit arguing, turn to page 35.*

■ *If you keep on arguing, turn to page 36.*

You are bound for Chicago carrying a small trunk, plus your lunch in a paper sack. Dreams are crowding your brain. How exciting it is to be going to a new city!

Your train races through the open prairie. You watch the telephone poles fly by. Now you see a few houses. You peer out at them, your nose pressed to the train window. To live in a house like those must be wonderful. Room to have a garden or plant a tree! Could such a thing be in your future?

When you reach Chicago, you find a small room. The rent is cheap enough. The room is not fine by any means, but it is much better than the tenement in New York.

Tomorrow you will look for work. Maybe you can be a clerk in one of those big stores.

You spend the next day looking for jobs. But the people behind the frosted glass in the stores look down on you. You wear shabby clothing. They think you are stupid. They don't want you clerking in their fine store. Or maybe they don't like Jews.

Finally you find a job in a small yardage store. You must show bolts of cloth to ladies who are very particular. Many of them are rich. They want just the right fabric. They must have just the right color.

"That clerk does not seem to understand what I want," an older woman complains to your boss. "Don't you have an American clerk who could wait on me?"

You cringe at the woman's words. You are going to night school to get rid of your accent. But it's hard.

Maybe the lady doesn't like you because you are Jewish! You remember how your parents suffered in the old country. There was a lot of anti-Semitism in Germany. That is one big reason why your father brought you to America. But there is probably some of it here too.

A man at the rooming house where you live has told you about a job at a hotel. He said it would be easy work. Perhaps you should quit this job at the yardage store before they fire you!

And yet, your boss has not complained about your work. Maybe you should just stick it out here.

■ *If you go to the hotel, turn to page 37.*

■ *If you remain at the yardage store, turn to page 38.*

"Oh, have it your own way," you say to your cousin. Maybe you are worrying too much. You spend the rest of the evening talking about your childhood memories of the old country.

You keep on working in the cotton factory, and the work grows easier. Or maybe you understand it better. Then one terrible day as you walk home from work, you find a stranger at your door. The sun has turned coppery in the smoky haze. You have an awful feeling that something bad has happened.

"Yes?" you say to the man.

"I am a foreman at the foundry. There has been an accident. Your cousin gave us this address. You are his closest relative living near here, I presume?" the man says.

"Yes, yes. Is it bad? How is he? Is he in the hospital?" you ask. Your heart is pounding.

The man does not want to tell you all the details. But your cousin is dead. And later on, you hear the awful details. His chest was crushed. His arms were broken. There was no chance to save him.

You bury your cousin in blessed Jewish ground. You say the kaddish (Jewish prayer for the dead) for him. The rabbi is very kind. But nothing can ease your sorrow.

For a whole year you work at the cotton factory. By then you are very good at English. Your night school teacher compliments you on your essays.

You get a new job working for the editor of a small Jewish newspaper. You spend most of your time running errands, but you learn a lot.

After two years you get to work for a publishing house in New York. This time you don't live in a tenement. You live in a nice apartment. You edit many books. Then you write a book of your own. It's the proudest day of your life when it's published. You dedicate it to your cousin who died in the foundry.

You have made your dreams come true.

■ *Turn to page 39.*

"You must follow your dream," you insist.

Your cousin throws up his hands. "Such a nagger you are! You remind me of my mama! I guess I could get a job at the glassworks. The money would not be so good as at the foundry. But I would be on my way to what I really want," he says.

When your cousin gets a job at the glassworks, you are so happy for him. You go to a small kosher (food prepared according to Jewish dietary law) restaurant to celebrate. You eat gefilte fish (chopped fish) and *leben* (goat's milk yogurt).

"I am not making cut glass like my father yet," your cousin says. "I am only a member of a team. The blower is the most important one. He is very skilled. He blows the pipe and makes the shapes. I am far from this. The gatherer brings the gob of hot glass from the furnace. I cannot even do this. I am only the worker at the furnace!"

"It's okay," you say. "Everybody has to start at the bottom. I am doing well in night school. My essays are very good, the teacher tells me. It awakens an old dream of mine. Maybe I will be a writer!"

You stay at the factory until you can get a job as a clerk in a publishing house. You don't do any real writing for a long time. Then, one day, you suggest an article. "I could write about how glass is made," you say.

Your editor lets you try to write a good article. You interview your cousin and find out all you can about glassmaking.

You are thrilled when your article is accepted!

One day your cousin comes to bring you a birthday gift. It's a beautiful set of stemware. You turn the delicate pink goblet around in your fingers. "Oh, how lovely it is," you gasp.

"I made it," says your cousin, his eyes shining.

You tell everyone you meet how proud you are of your cousin. He makes the most beautiful glassware in Pittsburgh. How happy you are that you talked him out of working at the foundry! A person must follow his or her dreams. You followed yours all the way to America. And it has been a good and exciting journey.

And the best is yet to be!

■ *Turn to page 39.*

You quit your job at the yardage store. You hurry to the hotel your neighbor told you about. A pleasant balding man hires you right away. It sure is easier work than lifting heavy bolts of cloth!

You try to be nice to the guests. One day the hotel manager asks you where you are from. You mumble, "Germany."

The man smiles and says, "Ah, German people are willing to work hard. I thought you were German. The Irish won't work as hard. I will not hire these Irish immigrants at all."

You feel sorry that he dislikes the Irish. He probably would dislike you too if he knew you were Jewish. You do not tell him. Why ask for trouble? You never talk about going to the temple or eating kosher food (food prepared according to Jewish dietary laws).

One evening while you are greeting new guests, a couple comes in the door. The man and woman look rich.

The hotel manager leans over to you and whispers, "Look at those two. They are Jewish social climbers. Very pushy. They know very well they are not welcome in this hotel. Yet they come in anyway just to throw their weight around."

You are amazed. Why are these nice-looking people not welcome? Suddenly they are before you. The hotel manager speaks harshly. "Gentiles [non-Jews] only here, please!"

How hurt and embarrassed the couple seem. The poor wife blushes red. They hurry away without another word.

"Look at them," mutters the manager, "acting as if they own the country. Sure, they have a lot of money. But we all know Jews don't get their money from hard work!"

You are boiling mad. "Yes, they do! Jews work very hard. Just like other people. My father was a peddler and he worked sixteen hours a day. And I work hard too. You see, I am Jewish. And I will not work here anymore!"

You rush from the place. The man is sputtering with shock. But you just cannot work for such a person! Never!

It is a full week before you find another job. But then you get a job in another hotel. You work hard and soon you are assistant manager. You are proud of yourself. You stood up for your principles.

■ *Turn to page 39.*

You decide to stay with the heavy bolts of cloth and the sometimes nasty customers. Sometimes your boss yells at you. Often the customers complain. Sometimes your boss and your customers yell at you at the same time.

But then, one day, your boss calls you aside. "You learn fast, kid. You're gonna get a promotion," he says. Your cigar-chomping boss grins then. "I'm sending you to New York to buy stock," he says.

You can't believe it! You are going back to New York on the railroad as a buyer. You are going back in style. You stay at a nice hotel. You look at fabrics and decide what to buy. You know a lot about fashions by now.

In two years you open up a little ready-to-wear shop in Chicago. You do poorly at first. You work seven days a week, sixteen hours a day. But then you begin to make much money. You seem to have a way of knowing what clothing will be popular next season.

"You're a genius," one of your customers tells you.

You laugh. You came into the clothing business by accident. But now it's very exciting. You wanted to be a writer once. But this is creative too. You are an artist with fabric. You design some dresses yourself, and they are very popular. You don't mind the long hours. You love the trips to New York. How different going there to buy is from living there in a tenement!

"This could never have happened to me in the old country," you tell a friend.

"Yes," your friend agrees. "Living in the dirty old tenements was worth it. We had to go through that to get here." Your friend is successful in business too.

"It is like my papa said," you remember. "Work hard and be honest, and success will come to you." You see your father's picture on the wall. He went through so much to bring his family to America.

On the anniversary of your father's death, you say the kaddish (Jewish prayer for the dead) for him. Then you smile and say, "Papa, thank you for bringing us to America. It's a beautiful land!"

■   *Turn to page 39.*

Jews in America

The first Jewish immigrants to America came very early. They were twenty-three Portuguese Jews who came in 1654. They settled in New Amsterdam (New York). They were not welcome. They were not even allowed to pray publicly. But slowly they gained their rights.

When the American Revolution started, two thousand Jews lived in America. One was Haym Salomon of Philadelphia. He gave seven hundred thousand dollars to the cause of American independence. Another Jew was David Emmanuel, who fought bravely during the siege of Savannah in the American Revolution. He was then elected governor of Georgia.

All through the years, Jewish immigrants have come to America for the same reasons all immigrants come. They longed for freedom and a chance to make the most of their lives.

Matching

1. The New York tenements were called

   _____ .

2. The first Jewish immigrants came to

   _____ .

3. The man who gave $700,000 to

   American independence was _____ .

4. The Jewish governor of Georgia was

   _____ .

5. The first Jewish immigrants came from

   _____ .

a) David Emmanuel

b) Portugal

c) New Amsterdam (New York)

d) Haym Salomon

e) dens of death

Group Activities

1. Many different immigrant groups came to America. Divide into about ten teams. With your teammates, report to the class on one of these immigrant groups.

2. Read the Emma Lazarus poem on the Statue of Liberty and discuss what it means today.

3. All of us (except the Indians) came from immigrants. Note the different groups represented in class on the chalkboard.

Individual Activities

1. Imagine you are an immigrant. Write a letter home about your experiences.

2. The tenement apartments where immigrants lived were very small. In one twelve-foot by twelve-foot room five families or twenty people lived. Using an inch to represent a foot, draw this room to scale. How much space did each person have? Where would you suggest the beds go?

3. Choose one of the following Jewish immigrants and write a short report:
   Haym Salomon   Benjamin Gratz   Uriah Phillips Levy   Rebecca Gratz

LAND RUSH

It's 1889 and you are heading for Oklahoma. A land rush is on. This is your big chance. A piece of land thirty miles wide and fifty miles long is being opened to land seekers. You want a nice farm of your own. You have been helping a friend farm in Kansas. All winter you have been dreaming of your own land in Oklahoma.

"Oklahoma has a good climate for growing," you say.

"And fertile soil," your friend says. "They have sparkling streams too. It's like a regular Garden of Eden."

You tried to go to Oklahoma before. A fellow named Dave Payne, a big, bold pioneer, led you and some others. But the United States Army stopped you. It was still Indian country then. Now the land is open to people like you.

"Plenty of folks will be running for land," your friend says. "Homeless folks. Speculators. Lot of them won't make it. But they'll be lined up to grab good land. You will have to scramble."

You nod. You really want a good piece. You must beat a lot of people to get it. It's going to be a wild race. About one hundred thousand people will be in the land rush. Some will be riding horses. Others will ride wagons or carriages, even bicycles. Some people will just go on foot. Trains will pull up and hundreds of folks will leap off and make the run.

"If I were you," says your friend, "I'd ride a horse. The wagons and carriages will crash into each other. The reins of the animals will all get tangled."

"Well," you say, "I might just go on foot. When all those horses start to whinnying and rearing up, it'll be crazy. I've always depended on my two

legs before. I can jump over tangled wagons and horses. I can run around obstacles."

"You're the biggest fool in the world," laughs your friend. "You'll never beat the horses on foot. You can't outrun horses and bicycles!"

"But some of the best pieces of land will be at the start of the race. All I need to do is spot a nice piece of land and claim it quick. I can do that afoot," you say.

But maybe your friend is right. What if the land is claimed quickly at the start? Then you'll have to go farther to get yours. And using a horse would be faster.

■ *If you go on foot, turn to page 43.*

■ *If you go on horseback, turn to page 44.*

Find out what your fate is!

You are ready to make the run on foot. You don't care what anybody says. This is too important to trust anything but your own two legs!

The pistol shot cracks in the air and you're off. From three sides, and three different entry points, they come. They're all screaming and hollering. The dust is so thick you think you might choke. The flowering prairie lies ahead, and your heart is pounding. A man pushing a wheelbarrow almost knocks you down, but you jump aside. You slip on a rock then and go sprawling. You scramble up, ignoring the pain in your ankle.

To your anger and amazement, you see people ahead of you. They've already made a claim! They have been here for hours. They sneaked in ahead of everybody else. Claim jumpers! Cheats!

"Cheatin' sooners!" gasps a man on a bicycle. He has a sign tied to his bicycle. It says "On to Oklahoma!"

All around you there's the crash of hammers. People are staking claims. Two men curse one another as they fight over a single homestead. The toss of a coin decides it. Just ahead, a wagon overturns, spilling pots and pans and chickens all over your path. You overleap the mad scene.

You see the land you want. It's a nice piece about a quarter of a mile ahead. You must run faster! There's a terrible ache in your chest. You feel your heart thumping. You choke on dust and stumble the last few yards. You grab for the hammer in the sack you carry.

"Hold it!" shouts a gruff voice. Another pioneer is about to drive a stake in the same piece of land!

"Whoa! This is mine!" you yell.

"I seen it first, boomer!" shouts the pioneer.

"No, I did!" you insist.

The truth is you both saw it at once.

You draw out a coin and say, "What do you say to a fair toss? What's your choice?"

"I'll take tails," says the pioneer, facing you.

The coin goes flying into the air. (Toss a coin at this point.)

■ *If it comes up tails, turn to page 45.*

■ *If it comes up heads, turn to page 46.*

The crack of a carbine held by a sergeant in the Third Cavalry starts the race. Every man, woman, and horse has been assigned a place to stand. The horse and bicycle riders are in the front row. You trust your brown gelding to carry you through. The buggies and lighter wagons are in the next row. The heavy teams are in the back. People on foot are off to the right, away from the horses and vehicles.

The rifle fires! You're off. The horses are rearing and bolting. You gelding is frightened by the melee. You are hurled to the ground. You have gone only three hundred yards. Your poor horse cannot go on. You must run forward alone. You carry a sack on your back containing a hammer and stakes. The clouds of choking dust from the wagons almost blind you.

You stumble in the path of an onrushing wagon. The driver screams at you. Your knees bloodied, you scramble to safety. To your left you see what looks like good farming land. It's level and it seems to have good grass. Maybe you ought to just stake your claim right here. You only need to run another few yards to do it.

You could never outrun the others to a choicer piece. Or could you? From the scent on the wind, you are pretty sure there's a creek to your right. A creek! A reliable year-round supply of water for your crops!

You remember the farm of your childhood in Indiana. One year there was a drought. The wells dried up. You saw the burning sun burn your crops to dust. You remember how you stood beside your weeping parents.

"Yonder there I could have had the Bailey farm. They got a creek, don'tcha know," your father said. "But I didn't take it. I went for this land instead. I never figured there'd be a drought . . . ."

Maybe you ought to make a run for the land with the nearby creek. Maybe you will end up getting nothing. Maybe by the time you get there all the creekside land will be claimed. But is it worth a try?

You have only a few minutes to make up your mind. Many folks are streaming toward the land to your left. Soon it will be taken.

■ *If you run to the creek, turn to page 47.*

■ *If you stake a claim to your left, turn to page 48.*

Tails! Your heart sinks. You have lost the piece of land you wanted. But all is not lost yet. You race on. Ahead is a mass of wagons and carriages. People are hammering in stakes everywhere. You grow desperate. Will you find nothing?

You see a lot that's been overlooked. You make a run for it. You never see the big black horse coming at your left. A flying hoof catches you in the side of your head. You fly, unconscious, into the dirt. Men and women hurry by. Nobody stops to help you. If they did, they would lose out too.

In about thirty minutes you wake up with a bad headache. You are not seriously hurt. But all around you is wild activity. The lucky ones who staked claims are raising tents. These will be their shelters until they can build houses. Before darkness falls, there are about 10,000 tents here.

You walk slowly back to the entry point.

"You lost out too, eh?" asks a thin-faced man. "I got busted farming in Kansas. Last summer the heat got us. Then that awful winter. I got no more fight in me. This was my last hope. I'm going back to Minnesota."

You can't go back to your home state of Indiana. There is nothing for you there. You turn around slowly. You drift back into the camp of the lucky landowners. Maybe you could find work.

"Need two willing hands?" you ask.

"Can you cook?" a man asks gruffly. "We need some folks to cook up a mess of food for the ones building."

"I can cook," you say.

Soon you are working. You make hundreds of pancakes and pies and loaves of bread for the hungry workers. You keep yourself busy until September of 1891. Then more land is opened in Oklahoma. This time you get a homestead. You plant cotton, corn, and row crops. You get married and have a son and a daughter. You don't get rich, but you have a good life. You sure are glad you hung around and waited for another chance at land.

You are part of the boom of Oklahoma.

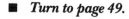 *Turn to page 49.*

Heads! "Hurrah!" you yell. You have won the land, fair and square. Soon you are putting up a tent for the night. Tents are springing up like mushrooms all around you. It's as if a city has been built in a day.

As darkness falls, you all become neighbors. You meet Miss Mabel Gentry of Neosha County, Kansas. She rode in on a spirited little black pony for seven miles to stake her claim.

"Now I'm an Oklahoma landowner," she says with a proud grin.

In the mad rush in, men gave no quarter to women. It was every boomer for himself or herself. You have to hand it to Miss Gentry. You feel proud and lucky that you made it too. Thousands didn't get any land. Now they wander around sadly. They have to go home empty-handed.

You start building your permanent home. You get married when it's finished. Then you put in crops. It's an exciting time for a while. Every day brings a new task. But then it gets boring and lonely. You haven't got much to do. You spend most Sundays just sitting on the fence staring down the road. You hope somebody comes along in a buggy. Then you and your spouse will have someone new to talk to.

"The farms are so far apart," your spouse says.

"Yes," you agree. You don't like farming in Oklahoma as much as you thought you would.

You're glad when oil is discovered in 1901. You sell your farm and buy a small oil company. Within the year you get a big strike. The oil is gushing from the Oklahoma soil.

"It sure beats corn!" you shout to your happy spouse. You both wallow around in the oil, laughing and getting dirty like children.

You can buy a nice home in Tulsa now. It's wonderful having close neighbors. You have many friends and you are never lonely again.

You're mighty happy you came to Oklahoma in the land rush. You are even happier that oil was found.

■ *Turn to page 49.*

You run for the creek land. But two other boomers beat you to it. You turn, wildly running off in another direction. Every time you reach a spot, it's taken! You see bicycle riders driving in stakes for their claims. How could they have beaten you? Everybody said the crisp grass of the prairies would be hard on bicycles. Yet they beat you on your horse. Even the buggy riders have land. Why did your horse have to stumble?

You are bitterly disappointed as the day goes on. All the lots have been taken. The lucky ones are already putting up tents. You sadly head back to the train station.

The northbound train is loaded with people like you. Their faces are long and sad.

"Where to now?" asks a would-be boomer.

You shake your head. You were so full of hope this morning. "I bought a fine, fast-looking horse. I saw folks with miserable old horses make it. I saw folks who ran in and got land. And my fine horse had to throw me off and ruin it for me. What bad luck!" you groan.

Your fellow loser nods. "Farming is no good anyhow anymore. Price of wheat has been going down since '81. Same for corn. The folks in the city call us rubes and hayseeds and most of the time we're busted," he says.

You agree. "If the south wind doesn't wither your crops, then the chinch bugs get them. I say if you can't lick 'em, join 'em. I'm moving to the city and try my luck there," you say.

"Doing what?" the other pioneer asks.

"I'll probably open up a little store . . . sell flour, salt, sugar," you say.

"I had a store in Ohio. I got a little money and some know-how," your new friend says.
"Maybe we could be partners?" you ask.

"Sounds good," he says.

You open up a small store in Tulsa and pretty soon you are doing well. You get a bigger store. Then you get two stores. You have a little chain of stores going before long.

"I'm sorta glad we lost out on land, partner," says the Ohio pioneer.

"Me too," you agree with a big smile.

■ *Turn to page 49.*

You race to the nearby spot and hammer in your stake. You can't believe your luck! You really own a piece of land! You stand there on the prairie grass, wild with joy.

"We made it!" you shout at your neighbor. He's driving in a stake too. Later on, you both raise tents. These will be your shelters until you build permanent houses.

You live in Oklahoma City with ten thousand others. You all live in tents. There's a lot of happy excitement. In just a few weeks you have a mayor. Why, it's a regular town out here!

You can already imagine the fields of grain sorghum growing on this fine land. You hurry to put in crops.

The first harvest is good, but the prices of grain are low. You don't make a profit. You must struggle just to keep going.

You hear about the Populist party. It's a group that fights for farmers. In 1892 you join up. A tall, nice-looking thirty-seven-year-old woman gets up to speak. She's a lawyer and the mother of four children.

"We farmers are being ruined by the railroads and loan companies," she says. "Let the bloodhounds of money beware! We farmers are going to stick together now."

"Listen to that," shouts an old farmer. He's just about clapping his hands off. You are too.

Soon you are very active in the Populist party. You and the woman who spoke, Mary Elizabeth Lease, work together. You get some important laws changed to help farmers. When Oklahoma becomes a state, you run for the House of Representatives. You get elected! You go to Washington to represent Oklahoma in Congress.

Farmers in Oklahoma and all over have a champion in you. Because of men in broad straw hats and tough-talking women in faded calico, times really change.

Your farm in Oklahoma never does make you rich. But you make a living and you continue your political career too. You are very proud to be fighting for farmers. They are just about the most important folks you know!

■ *Turn to page 49.*

Will Rogers

One of the best-known Oklahomans was Will Rogers. He was born near Claremore, Oklahoma. He was a cowboy and a circus performer. He was very proud to be part Cherokee. One of his favorite sayings was, "My ancestors did not come to America on the *Mayflower*. They met the *Mayflower*!"

Will was a much-loved humorist. He helped Americans laugh at themselves. He poked fun at politicians and at the ways of ordinary people. His most famous quote was "I never met a man I didn't like."

Will Rogers was a good example of the down-to-earth spirit of Oklahoma.

Matching

1. Will Rogers was born near

   _____ .

2. Rogers was proud to be part

   _____ .

3. About this number of people took part in

   the Oklahoma land rush: _____ .

4. The parcel opened to land seekers was 30 miles

   wide and this many miles long: _____ .

5. Land rushers came on horseback, by

   wagon, by bicycle, and _____ .

a) 50

b) afoot

c) Claremore

d) Cherokee

e) 100,000

Group Activities

1. Make some posters for the classroom containing short Will Rogers quotes.

2. Using a map, find the "Cherokee strip" in Oklahoma where the land rush was held. Find cities that were started by the land rush.

3. Make a land rush game on a large sheet of paper. Make as many paths leading to the land as there are students in your class. Make twenty segments for each path. Write in hazards such as "stumbled" and instructions such as "go back five spaces." Toss dice to advance. The first ten students who reach land are the winners. The rest get no land.

Individual Activities

1. Find out why Oklahoma is called the "Sooner" State. Write a paragraph about it.

2. If you could get a free piece of land today, where would it be? Describe your reasons for your choice in a paragraph.

3. Find the music for the play *Oklahoma!* and listen to *Oklahoma!* and *Oh, What a Beautiful Morning* to get the spirit of what the state is like.

Answer Key

1. North or South?

   1. b   4. e
   2. d   5. c
   3. a

2. After the Buffalo

   1. F   4. T
   2. F   5. F
   3. F

3. After the War

   1. e   4. c
   2. a   5. b
   3. d

4. Tenement Folk

   1. e   4. a
   2. c   5. b
   3. d

5. Land Rush

   1. c   4. a
   2. d   5. b
   3. e

Bibliography

1. North or South?

Angle, Paul M. *A Pictorial History of the Civil War Years.* Doubleday, 1967 (pp. 1–17).

Malone, Dumas, and Basil Rauch. *Crisis of the Union, 1841–1977.* Appleton-Century-Crofts, 1960 (p. 83).

2. After the Buffalo

Billington, Ray Allen. *Westward Expansion.* Macmillan, 1964 (pp. 657–59).

Hollon, W. Eugene. *Frontier Violence.* Oxford University Press, 1974 (pp. 135–36).

Joseph, Alvin M., Jr. *The Indian Heritage of America.* Bantam, 1968 (pp. 336–42).

Rothenberg, Jerome. *Shaking the Pumpkin.* Doubleday, 1972 (pp. 301–03).

Washburn, Wilcomb E. *The Indian and the White Man.* Doubleday, 1964 (pp. 377–85).

3. After the War

Duninng, William A. *Reconstruction, Political and Economic, 1865–1877.* Harpers, 1935 (pp. 71–85).

Morison, Samuel Eliot. *The Oxford History of the American People.* Oxford University Press, 1965 (pp. 705–20).

Woodward, C. Vann. *The Strange Career of Jim Crow.* Oxford University Press, 1966 (pp. 3–10).

4. Tenement Folk

"A Sweatshop Disaster." *Life Magazine* special report, "100 Events that Shaped America," 1975 (pp. 50).

Wade, Richard C. *Cities in American Life.* Houghton Mifflin, 1971 (pp. 127–29).

Weisberger, Bernard, ed. *The American Heritage History of the American People.* American Heritage Publishing Company, 1970 (pp. 252, 255, 293–45).

Wright, Kathleen. *The Other Americans.* Fawcett, 1969 (pp. 25–27, 33–37).

5. Land Rush

America, A Library of Original Sources. Vol. X. VFW, 1925 (pp. 22–27).

Billington, Ray Allen, *Westward Expansion.* Macmillan, 1964 (pp. 718, 723).

Hicks, John D. *The Populist Revolt.* University of Nebraska Press, 1961 (pp. 159, 244).

Hollon, W. Eugene. *Frontier Violence.* Oxford University Press, 1974 (p. 202).

Riegel, Robert. *America Moves West.* Holt, Rinehart and Winston, 1964 (p. 580).